SNOOPY,
COME HOME

SNOOPY, COME HOME

A NEW *PEANUTS* ® BOOK

by Charles M. Schulz

HOLT, RINEHART AND WINSTON

New York · Chicago · San Francisco

Library of Congress Catalog Card Number: 63-10087

Published, February, 1963
Seventh Printing, January, 1967

87752-1313

Printed in the United States of America

WHAT CAN YOU DO WHEN THE PATIENT DOESN'T SAY ANYTHING?

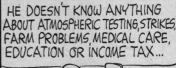

THAT LITTLE BUG LIVES IN A WORLD ALL HIS OWN..

HE DOESN'T KNOW ANYTHING ABOUT ATMOSPHERIC TESTING, STRIKES, FARM PROBLEMS, MEDICAL CARE, EDUCATION OR INCOME TAX...

ALL HE HAS TO WORRY ABOUT IS EATING AND GETTING STEPPED ON..

THAT'S THE SECRET...REDUCE YOUR WORRIES TO A MINIMUM!

THAT'S THE FIRST CLOUD I'VE EVER SEEN THAT WAS AFRAID OF HEIGHTS!

WHOEVER HEARD OF A CLOUD BEING AFRAID OF HEIGHTS?!

GET UP THERE WITH THE REST OF THE CLOUDS! THAT'S THE WAY! SHOW 'EM YOU'RE NOT AFRAID!

I GUESS IT IS RATHER SCARY WAY UP THERE!

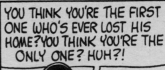

TO ME, THE UGLIEST SIGHT IN THE WORLD IS AN EMPTY DOG DISH!

I GET THE HINT!

MOST OF THE TIME I NEVER EVEN THINK ABOUT IT...

BUT EVERY NOW AND THEN IT BOTHERS ME...

MY KIND NEVER GETS TO EAT OFF FINE CHINA!

SCHULZ

THERE'S NO DOUBT MY ANCESTORS HAD A ROUGHER LIFE THAN I HAVE..

THEY HAD TO HUNT FOR THEIR MEALS, AND FIGHT JUST TO SURVIVE..

OF COURSE, I PUT UP WITH A LOT OF THINGS MY ANCESTORS NEVER DREAMED OF!

SCHULZ

WUMP!

REAL WHIRLYBIRDS DON'T GET THEIR EARS ALL TANGLED UP!

PUNT!

I HAD NO IDEA THAT PUNTING COULD BE SO SOUL-SATISFYING!

THAT'S ODD...

LAST NIGHT I LEFT MY FOOTBALL IN THE BACK YARD, AND THIS MORNING IT'S IN THE **FRONT** YARD...

VERY PECULIAR...

THE "MAD PUNTER" STRIKES AGAIN!

PUNT!

ROWF!

I DON'T SHARE MY PAD WITH ANYONE!

SNOOPY

SCHULZ

I DIDN'T SLEEP VERY WELL LAST NIGHT...

AND IT WAS **YOUR** FAULT! YOU AND YOUR STUPID BARKING!

THE WORST PART OF IT IS, YOU DON'T KNOW IF HE'S BARKING AT AN OWL, OR THE MOON OR A BURGLAR!

THAT'S ONE OF THE DRAWBACKS OF A LIMITED VOCABULARY!

SCHULZ

I BET I'D MAKE A PRETTY GOOD HOOD ORNAMENT!

MY GLASSES! I CAN'T FIND MY NEW GLASSES!

THE OPHTHALMOLOGIST WILL KILL ME IF I'VE LOST MY NEW GLASSES!

DON'T WORRY...SOMEBODY WILL FIND THEM, AND BRING THEM BACK TO YOU...

SEE? WHAT DID I TELL YOU?

OH, THIS IS AN IDEAL RABBIT-CHASING DAY!

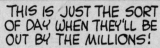

THIS IS JUST THE SORT OF DAY WHEN THEY'LL BE OUT BY THE MILLIONS!

C'MON, SNOOPY, LET'S GET OUT AND SNIFF THOSE RABBITS!

YOU DON'T SNIFF RABBITS, YOU **SEE** THEM!

SCHULZ

ALL RIGHT! LET'S HAVE THOSE GLASSES!

GOOD GRIEF! IF IT ISN'T ONE THING, IT'S ANOTHER!

HE WAS JUST JEALOUS BECAUSE I LOOKED SO DISTINGUISHED!

SCHULZ

YOU DON'T KNOW IT, BUT YOUR TROUBLES ARE JUST BEGINNING!

WHY WOULD ANYONE WANT TO LEAVE A NICE TREE LIKE THAT?

MINE IS THE SORT OF HOME WHERE FRIENDS FEEL THEY CAN JUST DROP IN ANY TIME

SCHULZ

IT'S NICE TO HAVE A HOME WHERE YOUR GUESTS FEEL COMFORTABLE

SCHULZ

MY HOME IS ALWAYS OPEN TO THOSE WHO ENJOY DISCUSSION GROUPS!

ARF!

SOONER OR LATER YOU GET TIRED OF HAVING SO MUCH COMPANY!

DON'T DO ANYTHING YOU MIGHT REGRET!
!

THAT'S GOOD ADVICE

IT'S DISGRACEFUL THE WAY YOU HANG AROUND ALL DAY DOING NOTHING!! NOW YOU GET OUT THERE, AND CHASE SOME RABBITS!

ARF ARF ARF

YOU'RE NOT FOOLING ANYBODY BUT YOURSELF!

IT'S A STORM AT SEA!

THE FIERCE GALE LASHES THE RAIN INTO THE FACE OF THE CAPTAIN AS HE STANDS ON DECK!

DON'T YOU LOVE THE FEEL OF A SOFT, GENTLE SUMMER SHOWER?

SIGH

"AND HE HUFFED AND HE PUFFED, AND HE BLEW THE HOUSE DOWN!"

THAT'S RIDICULOUS! HOW COULD A WOLF BLOW A HOUSE DOWN?

SCHULZ

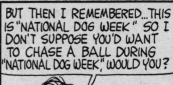

MY HOME IS A HAVEN FOR ALL SORTS OF WEARY TRAVELERS!

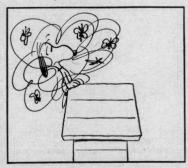

KLUNK!!

STUPID BUTTERFLIES!

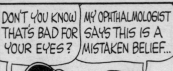

PUNT!

PURE SATISFACTION!

ALL OF EARTH'S CREATURES HAVE, HIDDEN WITHIN THEIR BEINGS, A WILD UNCONTROLLABLE URGE TO **PUNT!**

WHENEVER A SHOW COMES ON ABOUT HUNTING, I LEAVE!

ARF ARF ARF ARF

"BARKING DOGS NEVER BITE"

WHY DO YOU SUPPOSE THAT IS, CHARLIE BROWN?

I DON'T KNOW... MAYBE IT'S JUST A SAYING...

NO, IT'S BECAUSE IT'S A REAL GOOD WAY TO BITE YOUR TONGUE!

I THINK THAT'S RATHER NICE..

THEY ALWAYS OPEN THEIR MEETINGS WITH A SONG!

THEIR MEETINGS ARE BECOMING MORE AND MORE FREQUENT..

THEY USUALLY DON'T LAST VERY LONG, HOWEVER

THEN AGAIN THEY SOMETIMES DON'T BREAK UP 'TIL MIDNIGHT!

IT WAS NICE OF THEM TO ASK ME, BUT I JUST HAD TO SAY, "NO"

I SUPPOSE BECAUSE THEY USE MY PLACE FOR THEIR MEETINGS THEY FELT OBLIGATED TO ASK ME TO JOIN THEIR GROUP

SCHULZ

I WONDER IF IT WOULD BE WRONG FOR ME TO LISTEN-IN ON ONE OF THEIR MEETINGS!?

THAT'S THE MOST FRIGHTENING THING I'VE EVER HEARD!

SCHULZ

I HATE FALL!

SOMETIMES I THINK I'D LIKE TO LEAVE THIS PLACE...

I'D JUST LIKE TO GET AWAY, AND GO OUT AND SEE NEW THINGS AND MEET NEW PEOPLE

BUT THERE'S ALWAYS SOMETHING THAT KEEPS ME HOME..SOMETHING THAT MAKES ME STAY...

THAT OL' SUPPER DISH!

That's the closest I'll ever come to kicking a pig!

If you're looking for an apple, I ate the last one..

Boy, if you weren't wearing glasses, I'd slug you a good one!

Glasses are good for your eyes... they keep you from getting punched in them!

THIS IS SERIOUS...HOW CAN YOU HELP SOMEONE WHO HAS BECOME A COMPULSIVE "WATER SPRINKLER-HEAD STANDER"?
IT'S VERY SIMPLE...JUST TURN OFF THE WATER!
SCHULZ
THANK YOU..
SIGH

LISTEN TO THIS, CHARLIE BROWN...
IT SAYS HERE THAT THERE ARE OVER SIX HUNDRED AND SEVENTY THOUSAND DIFFERENT KINDS OF INSECTS!
WOW!
TAKE COMFORT, LITTLE FELLOW.. YOU ARE NOT ALONE!
SCHULZ

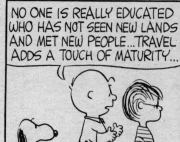

A GOOD MANAGER LEARNS TO MAKE THE BEST USE OF WHATEVER MATERIAL HE HAS!

RATS! I'LL NEVER BE ABLE TO GET A SUN TAN!

WITH A LITTLE PRACTICE I BET I COULD GET THE SHOES, TOO!

SCHULZ

PTUI!!

I WORRY ABOUT WHO'S GOING TO SEE HIM FIRST...A BIG-LEAGUE SCOUT OR THE HUMANE SOCIETY!

SCHULZ

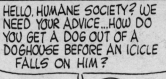

THEY NEVER EVEN SAID, "GOOD-BYE"

HOW ABOUT THAT?

I LET THEM BUILD THEIR NEST ON TOP OF MY DOGHOUSE, I BABY-SIT FOR THEM, I HELP TEACH THE LITTLE ONES TO FLY...

AND NOW, ALL OF A SUDDEN, THE WHOLE FAMILY JUST **LEAVES** !! NO "THANK YOU'S"... NO "GOOD-BYE'S"... **NOTHING!** BIRDS DRIVE ME CRAZY!

AND THE WORST PART OF IT IS, THEY CAN FLY, AND I CAN'T!